Contents

The Crossing of Doom

Crossing Lily

On the way back to base ...

A long time later ...

Go to 12

Spot the Kids

Spot the kids in this comic so far ...

At the end, look back
and do it again!

The Crossing of Doom

Back at base ...

What is the problem with Crossing Lily?

Well, one night, I visited ...